Nuggets for Thought

A Mother and Daughter's Collection of
Poems, Reflections and Flash Fiction
About the Life They See

"Consider carefully your choices..."

LYVITA BROOKS

Copyright © 2023 by Lyvita Brooks

Published by LRW Publication, LLC
www.lrwpublicationllc.com
Our mission is to provide tools to help Believers grow in love with God, their neighbor, and themselves.

Printed in the United States of America

ISBN: 978-1-889003-12-2

Other Resources for support:
www.lyvitabrooks.com (Website)
Hanging Out With Jesus Podcast (Podcast and YouTube Channel)
@hangingoutwithjesuspodcast (Instagram)
To order additional copies of this book or permission requests, go to:
www.lyvitabrooks.com

Interior Design by FormattedBooks.com

Dedication

VERDELL REESE

Ma, I finally kept my promise.
Your writings are now published.

CONTENTS

Poems by Lyvita Brooks

Flash Fiction by Lyvita Brooks

At The End Begins Another's Future

Beginnings

MY MA, VERDELL REESE

How can I tell you about my Ma without crying? This is hard but I have to do it because I need to keep my promise. A promise to publish her writings. And yet, it's a promise to fulfill to myself because I was raised by a woman who kept her promises and never quit.

I'm an only child, born to the youngest of nine children, who everyone adored. And yet, I also see her as a Miss-Know-it-All. Now I'll probably get in trouble for writing that last statement because to family and friends she was awesome. The perfect Auntie, friend, and advisor. Yet to me, she was my competition. My inspiration.

Ma grew up in South Carolina with parents and grandparents who were churchgoers that loved the Lord. She worked in the family dry cleaning business all through school. After graduating from Benedict College as a P.E. Teacher, she taught in South Carolina, Washington DC, and Philadelphia, PA. She'd often say, "I'm not a gym teacher, that's the part of the building I work in. My profession is Physical Education teacher." In college she met her best friend, my godmother, Pearlie Mac. Shortly afterwards she met Hayward, then I was born. I'm the result of college sweetheart love.

Education was a big part of my Ma's life. Even after Ma retired she kept learning. She attended classes to teach Vacation Bible School and graduated from New Life Bible Institute at Liberty Baptist Church in Philadelphia, PA. She was in her sixties when she became the director and teacher of Vacation Bible School at her church. I believe education was the motivation that sparked her to write. Many of the topics she wrote about centered on education, discipline, or not quitting.

She was famous for saying, "Either you do or you don't," when she was edging you to do the right thing. Another saying was, "You already know what 'don't' looks like, so why not try another way?" We'd often hear,

"Quitting isn't an option." And her famous one, "If you have a job, you can get what you want." This coming from a woman who would give you her last dollar only to discover later that she had a ten or five dollar bill tucked away in a discarded purse. I remember special occasions, like when a lady gave her twenty dollars in the store so she could get a dress she wanted. Seriously, things like that happened to her many times. She'd often say, "Most people who are born on the thirteen have bad luck, but I've found blessings."

One of the most endearing qualities my Ma had was the ability to make you feel hopeful. She was able to convince you that you were important and the world needs you. That you weren't just here to be here. Everyone's got a purpose. Everyone's got a struggle. The struggle is to let you know what you are made of. Ma had a way of bringing "trusting on Jesus" in the conversation without making you feel awkward. Her love always shined through. I guess that's why babies always wanted to go to her. It's also why when my cousins' mothers passed, they all seemed to gravitate to Ma. Even though they took up my time with her, I couldn't complain (but as an only child you know I had to) because I felt and knew that she loved me. I hope her writings will cause you to pause and reflect on whether the choices you made were wise or adjustments are needed.

Ma married her longtime friend and the man I call Dad, Richard, when I was in elementary school and then later separated when I was in middle school. To an only child this was to my advantage. I did try to play them between each other until my Dad said, "No you can't come over. Settle it with your mother." OK, that wasn't the right answer, but it was the best answer. One thing for sure, Ma always said, "I have a job. I can take care of my child and me." No wonder between Ma and Dad, I grew up to be an independent woman who loves the Lord and still works. And yet, I am my mother's child, because she was a strong independent Black woman who loved her family, her family's friends, her friends, and adored children. I found my mother writing a lot after I got married. She even shared a few with me. We laughed and sometimes wrote together, exchanging our joy of the written word.

During her final years upon this earth, I saw my Ma endure much pain, but now that I look back, she did it with grace. She didn't complain but I did, to the nurses, doctors and to our God. So I learned to be strong. Ma didn't write, anymore, and neither did I. We talked, watched TV, sat with Auntie Rudine, laughed with family and friends that called or stopped by. We didn't write but I gained more insight into the life of a woman I knew would never die.

And yet when Jesus took her home, He never left my side. He helped me understand why everything has a season. My Ma's was done here on earth, but mine was just beginning. Life might look hopeless without her, but I'm not to shy away. Ma raised a woman of God, who for a season leaned heavily on Jesus, relying on Him, as I watched Him hold me up with loving arms and held my hand like a little child's. I have a purpose and I can't let my Ma nor Jesus down. Ma's passing wasn't my ending. It was both our beginnings, only apart. Now, I write.

I'd love to tell you more about my Ma but after five years of being without her, it still brings tears of joy but also the ache of missing her. I find comfort in knowing she is with the Lord as I wrap myself up in her blankets. Maybe someday, I will write her story, but for now, I just wanted you to know a little about her and why I had to publish her writings. She truly was a woman with nuggets to live by.

MA'S NOTEBOOK

On the main floor of her row house, sits the mustard-colored wing chair, covered in plastic where she sat to watch TV and write.

A small wooden stool clings to its side by the many juice spills and food add-ons. Her Bible is still lying there, atop it is the notebook.

It beckons me to read. To finish the journey I promised her before she passed.

Opening the water-stained, crumbled, sticky, and wrinkled pages, I find scribbled dark black ink, set into strokes that formed words I can understand, but some thoughts are incomplete.

Each page holds a memory, a story formed through hidden experiences. I only got a glimpse. A laugh, a comment, a lifeline to the life she lived.

Browsing through her poems. Reflecting on half shared thoughts. Pondering questions we discussed when she was alive. Tearing, thinking of the good times we had.

I promised to publish her writings someday. How could I keep my promise? Her writing was unfinished. When her physical life ended at seventy-seven, she started her spiritual life with her Savior for all eternity. Her work on earth was finished. Now mine's begun.

It's been a long time coming. It was meant to be. A mother and daughter's writings about the life they see.

Reflections and Poems

BY VERDELL REESE

BUILDING BRICKS FOR STEPS TO STAND ON IN LIFE

By Verdell Reese

In life each person has his own road to travel.
The road is bricks of life, stepping stones, to the stars.
Each time you get closer to the stars, the wind blows harder.

A brick of life is made completing a class in school or learning a new rule.
Each morning you step out of bed you begin to build a brick.
As the bricks come together, you have a step on which to stand in life.

You are key to your life.
Each brick is a key for you.
Without a brick to stand on, your foundation is broken,
life yields ups and downs.

Complete the development of each brick by all means necessary.
Each time you get closer to the stars, the wind blows harder.
Use discipline and perseverance.

Family members have stacked strong bricks to get you started
and give you a push. Now you are at the age to stand alone,
reaching for your own stars, and the wind blows harder.

You must choose. You are key to your life.
Every brick for your family and you.

Step forward? Step Backward? Stand still? Go sideways? Right? Or left?

Every decision is based on a brick. Every brick becomes a step to stand on.

Every step gets you closer to the stars, where the wind blows harder.

VOICES OF REFLECTION

By Verdell Reese

My thinking reflects who I am.
My thinking reflects what I do.
What is more important?
Who I am or how I act?
Does who I am reflect how I act?
Or how I act reflect who I am?
Am I somebody?
Am I what my parents intended?
How can I tell?

By looking back or forward.
Am I what my child think I should be?

I am somebody.

Is it important for me to know who I am?
Then maybe I can determine how I act.
Is this the time to assess myself?
I am somebody.
Are my friends who I think they are?
Are my friends what I see?
Can my friends determine how I act?
Am I what my friends think I should be?

I am somebody.
To gather a reflection of me, I have to extend myself
and compute my assessment.

Can this be done or should I just look into a mirror?
Is my reflection what I see, what I think, or how I act?

A STORY OF LOVE

BY VERDELL REESE

She lived a structured life.
She followed the correct procedures.
She was failing in her heart.

He didn't care.

She had to leave, but who was he to stay, was there a price to be paid?
Did she deserve more or did she deserve less? If they was
satisfied why should they try to decide on who should
stay or who should go or even get a divorce?

Her family was her life.
Did she have to pay a price?
They both had to agree that their relation-
ship would hurt someone to some degree.
They both had to go.

Both followed their hearts.

Songs were sung, pleasures erased, hearts cried, laughter contained.

The egg-stepping stage of life lasted until the separation
was final and they followed their hearts.

TRY

BY VERDELL REESE

Today you do,
Tomorrow you don't

Today you can,
Tomorrow you won't

And now you may,
But then you shouldn't

You want to catch a ride,
But it's up too high

Should you reach up and pull it down?
Or should you climb up and stay?

You see a dime on the floor, right by your foot…
Can you use it? How can it help?

You have to find a way within yourself to use
what you have to help yourself.

How?

If you do on the days you don't, then when you should, you can.

You can survive
Only if you try.

DARKER THAN ME

By Verdell Reese

Everybody in my family is darker than me (that's not true)
Everybody in my family has color.
Three of us are darker and six of us are lighter
Can the color of your skin make a difference in your life?
I don't know because I've only had one color.

I don't think so if you don't let it.

I know this is a very sensitive topic to write about but to me we are all family. As I become older, others tried to make a difference in us (Black Pete). In my family, everyone had to follow the same rules.
Can the color of your skin make a difference in your life?

I don't know because I only had one.

Others sometimes tried to make a difference in us as I grew up. I had to follow the rules because I didn't want to disappoint my Daddy. I was going to be the best me I could be. All through high school, my sister and I were known as my brother's sisters. No names (sister), can the color of your skin make a difference in your life?

I don't know, I've only had one color but I don't think so. It's how you think about it.

In the big world, we live in the color of our skin. It does make a difference. But in the world of my family I don't think it does because we each only have one color. If you were taught by your parents that you are somebody, you will feel like you are somebody.

Not just sister.

But I have to admit my life was a little different because I was the youngest of nine children. Ninth in a multicolored family. Some call us Black, others African Americans, does it make a difference in the color line? Does it hinder or help in our family to be called Black or African American or just family?

When I had my first child I was sitting across the heater feeding my baby with my cousin. He said, "They said you had a baby. Where is your baby? I thought your baby would look different. I didn't think that was your baby."

I said, "Yeah, this is my baby."

When my daughter was around two years old she came home and said "Mom, I'm grayer than you." Someone had told her about color but she did not remember the color.

As I was growing up, I had other problems. My brother would say go to the store and get me some ice cream and cake. I was happy because I knew I was going to have some too… When he returned from the store I said, "Can I have a piece of cake?" He said, "No because you used incorrect English. You should have said 'may I have a piece of cake.' You cannot have any this time. You will have to wait until the next time." I did not get any cake or ice cream that day.

Can the color of your skin make a difference in your life? I don't know because I've only had one color.

The color of your skin can make a difference in your life because we live in a prejudiced society. It's your family that can make a diffcrence. If everyone is taught to love and respect others, this world would be a peaceful place to live in.

ARE YOU A SEPARATOR OR
A PEACEMAKER?

BY VERDELL REESE

What is the difference?

One is alone.

The other helps others.

One feels that they are blessed to take care of themselves and their families.

The other feels like they are blessed to be alive to care for themselves and help others in need. They help fix problems or things because of love and not self.

Communication is key. You can't help someone by not talking to them.

Forgive and forget.
Life moves on.

Life is a continuous challenge.
It will not stop because you are angry.
Be the best that you can be.

Do you solve problems or do you create problems?

Evaluate yourself, sometimes it's not always others. Where is your part of the blame? No one is perfect.

You do not live in this world alone, you have to live with others.

All families need peacemakers not separators.

BECAUSE
(I WANT TO)

By Verdell Reese

If I do what I want to do and not what I should do—will I feel stress?
What I should do may cause the stress because it did not win.

Will I ever be free to do what I want to do without regrets?

Every action causes a reaction. If what I choose is positive, I get a
reward. If I make a choice and it is negative, I have a responsibility.

I have to decide on the type of environment I need
to maintain in order to survive or thrive.

Can I live with violence, profanity, or without love?

When I have a choice, I know what I should do, but
most of the time I do what I want to do.

Sometimes I am very happy, other times I am very sad.

I made the choice, I have to be able to deal with the consequences.

How I deal with the consequences determines my lifestyle.

Happiness - sadness = sickness or wellness?

I can choose to be happy or sad.

I Can!

DID I WIN

By Verdell Reese

I told Janet that I cursed Karen out, but Janet said no because Karen said she cursed me out.

Did I win?

If we both used the same words…who wins?

If I use the words first…will I win?

How do we determine the Winner? The vocabulary is so limited; who wins?

I called Karen the basic names. I told her what she could do for me and what I would do for her.

Did I win?

Karen called me the basic names and said I could do the same for her.

Did I win?

How do we determine the Winner or Loser?

Do I have to fight to win?

If I lose the fight, can I win the cursing out?

SOMETHING TO THINK ABOUT

By Verdell Reese

What type of discipline are you using on your children?
Do you have a system?
Do you have goals for your children?
Do they understand the goals?

Are you doing things to help them achieve their goals?
Are you considering their abilities?
Do they understand abilities and gifts?
Are your goals realistic for your child?

Are you teaching your child the things you think they should know?
Can you change the atmosphere of your family?
Who has to change now?
Do you love all your children but dislike some of their ways?

Do you worry about them caring for themselves later in life?
Are parents supposed to guide their children?
Who is at fault if your child do not perform the way you want them to?
Did your system of discipline hinder or help your child?

Whose fault is it?

Be aware that your children will have a discipline system for you. Example:
"You don't listen to me."

THE TEACHER

By Verdell Reese

Is my child learning from me or from the teacher?
I told him to come inside before dark. It was dark. I went to the door and I said bring your *** in here now. He came inside quickly.

Is my child learning from me or the teacher?
Once inside, I cursed him out. I stopped only because he reminded me that I did not have any cigarettes and he would go to the store for me. He is such a sweet child to think about me. I let him go in the dark because it's just down the street.

Is my child learning from me or the teacher?
When we were eating, he spilled some food on the floor. I said calmly, pick it up. He did not move. I looked at him, and I became angry. I said ***pick the *** up now. He picked it up quickly and put it in the trash.

Is my child learning from me or the teacher?
He woke up about 3:00 in the morning and asked if my boyfriend would be staying for the night. I said, what is it to you? He said, tell me. I want to know. I said, go to bed. He said, I'm not sleepy and sat down to watch TV. I said ***get the *** out of here now. He left the room quickly.

Is my child learning from me or from the teacher?

The teacher called and said my son is very disruptive in school. He will not listen. He uses profanity excessively. I thought, *What the *** you telling me for, you the TEACHER?*

Is my child learning from me or from the teacher?
When he returned from school, I cursed him out for acting like a fool in school and having the teacher call me about his ***.

Is my child learning from me or from the teacher?

Am I the teacher?

Cursing out your children demeans them early in life.

Why can't you see it?

AM I RESPONSIBLE?
IT'S NOT MY FAULT.

By Verdell Reese

My child is my most valued possession. I love her.
I taught her to walk, to talk, and use the potty.
Am I responsible? It's not my fault.

I can remember her first words DA DA, MA MA
It was so cute when she would repeat words after me.
Did I teach her to use profanity too?
Am I responsible? It's not my fault.

I received a call from school.
Saying my child was suspended and they were sending her home.
I said no, I will come to school to get her.
Am I responsible? It's not my fault.

When I arrived at school, I asked,
Why is my child suspended?
She is a good child and she listens to me.
I was ready to cuss the teacher out.
I walked over to my child and I said why?
She said, "Ma, it's not my fault."
The teacher asked me to move back into my seat.
As I was moving I said to Lisa, "I hate that ***. I wasn't even talking to her."
Mom, it is not my fault.

Am I responsible?
It's not my fault.
Then who?

UNTITLED

By Verdell Reese

Be aware that your children will have a discipline system for you. Example: you don't listen to them.

Can you think of some type of discipline?

1. hitting
2. cursing
3. feeling sorry for me (mommy)
4. ignoring
5. put down system
6. encouragement
7. reward system

Do you and your partner have the same goals for your children?
Did you discuss it with her or him?

Do you discipline your child according to your feelings…?

WHY NOT CLOSE THE SCHOOLS?

By Verdell Reese

Some teachers are teaching
Some students are learning

Some teachers are not teaching
Some children are not learning

Is this a sign of the times?

To teach is to inspire.
To learn is to continue a process in many different stages
to inspire is to start the process.

The benefits of learning are to improve self-worth and to understand the importance of caring for others.

Are our schools responsible for the self-worth of our children?

We are all teachers.
We teach, profanity — love — hate — violence and about God.
We teach, what our children experience and see from birth to death. As adults, we teach a lifestyle of self-worth or self-defeat.

Take a look at yourself, through the eyes of a young child, or imagine, if you can, what our schools are responsible for teaching to inspire students for success in all areas of life.

Is that an impossible task?

Why not change the goals of our schools?

You can blame me, and I can blame you, but the children are still watching and learning...*what?*

25% OFF

By Verdell Reese

Am I living my life to its fullest or am I 25% off?
Do I feel 100% today?
Yesterday I felt tired. Did I lose 25%?

My sister made me angry.
I felt less than 25% off.

What happens to my 100% if I don't use it up every day?

If I have a very happy day, I used up the balance.

What decreases my %?
Is it stress—emotions or intellect?

The relationship between emotions and intellect can cause mental stress.

If I use only my intellect all day, will I use 100%?

If I use only my emotions all day, will I lose 25%?

If I could find a way to combine my intellect with my emotions, without stress, would I be able to achieve 100% or would I still be 25% off?

BLESSED

By Verdell Reese

I want to cry
But I shouldn't
I can, but I won't
It's hard to cry if you are not very sad
If you feel blessed, then why complain?

Am I alone? Is God with me? How can I tell?
I feel His presence in my life
The Bible is my daily guide

Are you a believer?
Stop and think
If you plan your future with God
You will learn the dos and the don'ts
Experience the ups and the downs.

The daily quality of your life will improve. It's worth a try. When you give money in church, you are giving it to God. Don't complain about how others use your money. It is your gift to God to show your appreciation for His gifts to you and the world.

HABITS

BY VERDELL REESE

We are all connected by habits. We are all concerned about the difference in races, but all races have similar habits. Instead of judging others on how they look, their color, or age, judge them on what they do, their habits. Let's try grouping people according to their habits.

Smokers—drinkers—drug users—sex pots—overeaters—gum chewers—Christians—profanity users—music lovers. We believe there are good habits and bad habits. We would have groups of good people and groups of bad people.

What group would you be in?

Do you have a secret habit?

WHO AM I?

By Verdell Reese

I am what I want to be, I am, can't you see?
Are you what you want to be, are you who I see?
I like who I am.
I do—can't you tell?
My feelings change when I hurt, can't you tell?
When I eat I gain weight, I do, can't you see?
I forgot to take a bath last night—O no—do I smell?
When something is wrong with me, you can
always see, smell, or tell, you can.
I can be what I want to be. I will, you will see, I can.
Sometimes my thoughts are not very clear,
but you are always there, you are.
You help me make poor decisions sometimes.
I can tell you don't care, I can.
You help me to make good decisions sometimes.
I am so proud that you are near, I am.
But that is because you are my inner self,
                        You are me.

LIFE CIRCLES

BY VERDELL REESE

We are all rounded and joined together by love circles.

Life is a circle because it keeps going around.

Caring — sharing — receptive — receiving and
giving makes our lives complete.

When a person leaves the circle it is because
their job is complete. They are made whole.

Life's waters will cleanse their spot because their goals are completed.

When a circle is broken because of death it
is the removal of the complete circle.

Your circle will always be remembered because of
the showers of love you have spread every day.

Love circles are everywhere as expressions of life or love.

Our circles are bonded together by love.

When the rain showers come the love circles
swell and become closer together.

We are all rounded and bonded together by love circles.

When a circle is completed it moves up higher with the older circles
to look back down on us or to act as a go-between to weather the storms.

Love is from everlasting to now.

Life is the remembrance of each other.

Our lives are in our thoughts.

A LOST CHARACTER

BY VERDELL REESE

There are certain attributes, traits that should always remain in our society:

1. Respect
2. A spirit of giving, sharing or helping others
3. Respect for yourself, others, and things
4. Honoring God

Poems

BY LYVITA BROOKS

A POEM

A Poem expresses our passions,
    gives voice to our ideas

A Poem verbalizes our perceptions,
    our consciousness about this world

A Poem reveals our fears,
    evolved from the stories we tell ourselves

A Poem exposes our beliefs,
    sets forth the truth of who we are

A Poem verbalizes our existence,
    uttering, "Here we are!"

BUT A DREAM

You come to me in the warm solitude of the night,
    slipping inside my dark brown eyes
    developing vivid pictures for my delight.

You come again in the bright calming sun,
    causing droopy eyes to gaze upon
    flashing pictures on the run.

You also come at my lonely dull hours,
    pricking my thoughts of promising desires
    that infiltrate my eyes to see tomorrows.

You allow me pleasure
    and despondency,

You allow me thrills
    and anxiety,

You allow me personality alterations
    and reality.

                You are but a dream!

Published in *Poetic Voices of America* Fall 1997 Anthology

THE UNSELFISH ME

I have a problem
    it's with my mind
I think wrong things
    from time to time

I laugh at unhappy situations
    and cry only when I hurt
I get bored with visitors
    who stay to long

I feel sorry for myself
    I do things without thinking first
    I do things without caring last

I am someone
Searching to find…the unselfish Me
I define me to be

Then I accept Jesus as my LORD, my Savior, my King

I have a problem
    grasping that God's designed me
My thinking changes of me
    As I study the Holy Bible

Because I'm no longer looking for the unselfish Me
God's already defined me…the who I am to He.

MARRIED SINGLE WOMAN

I'm a married single woman
without legal papers
common law marriage, but not in our state
wedding ring dangled in my face
pretending to be... I'm really not his wife.

I'm a single woman
loving hard
working to keep our relationship alive
taking care of children that aren't even mine
blinded by the green grass on the other side.

I'm a woman
of hope
waiting for that ring and Mrs. before my name
living a lie, pretending to be married
if he dies, I have no hope of claiming any of his things.

I am
committed like a married woman
determined to make this work
chained to an idea that eludes me
thinking, "Princesses don't live like this."

SINGLE MARRIED WOMAN

I'm a Single Married Woman
caught between my desires and the reality of a lie
loved only when needed
tossed away when convenient
raising children that I can't discipline

I'm a Married Woman
committed to a man
who leaves more than stays
I'm free to be me
and yet he doesn't know me

I'm a Woman
caught between the bills
and the lifestyle he gives
come and go as I will
he keeps his distance living in the basement

I am
loved from afar
validated when it doesn't affect his ego
left alone so he can do his own thing
bought out to show off

I'm Vashati, from the Bible
I'm his Queen
Thinking, "I didn't signed up for *this*?"

COMPLEX WOMAN

Living fake lives
No ring
No papers
Playing married games
hoping the 7 year law kicks in

My mother would be ashamed
If she wasn't doing her own thing
Divorced twice
with married papers it never lasts

I'm a single married woman
Committed by my words, but is he?
Don't care cause he knows I love him
even if he don't love me

Children confused on parenthood
Blended family
Kids living in different spots—weekend house guest
Are we family or not?
Relationships twisted, mangled, and stressed
Who is my mommy? Who do I believe? Where is my daddy?

A single married woman
Pretending all the time
Acting married but got no grounds
Do her own thing without permission
Remembering that there is a thin line

He could leave at anytime

What happens when he dies?
Am I his wife, finance', or girlfriend?
Truth be told
I'm his in-house sex partner
Appease me, Brother!

Angry words
Caught in a lie
Money problems
His integrity is fake
The relationship falters
and kids pick sides

Now what
Do I leave
Do I stay
Do I teach my daughters that this is the way
Living as a single married woman
continuing to lie in her face

My grandmother would be happy
If I changed my ways
Marriage with papers were solid back then
The world's changing
Today we do our own thing
determining right from wrong and our identity

My choice
Keeping options open
This is who I am
I am a complex
Single married woman
(period)

THE MIDDLE MAN

He's left me again
Alone with his child
Locked in separate rooms
Quiet as a mouse

No relationship
The middle man is our only connection
She there, I here
It's safer that way

Timed bathroom assignments
Small talk and respectful smiles
Always visible to his critiquing eyes
Too much talking will open the scares

Again he's left me
Alone in my room
His child across the hall
Whispers, tears, neither of us move

My door opens
He enters laughing
I dare dialogue
The room becomes unwelcoming

He talks to us separately
Voices are low

He keeps us worlds apart
Connected to himself by the web of fear laced over our hearts

He is clueless to the hope we seek
The distance he demands to keep
Feeling trapped in a maze, cautious all the time
Like a mother's heart, torn from her child

He is a musician with a control panel
Dials, knobs, levers, buttons
Designed to keep his music and us
In step to his pace

GRANDMA AGGIE

I tell the gospel truth
    Of a virtuous woman
Dressed in the finest apparel
    Stitched by hands with care
Honored by all her children
    And husband who loves her dear.

I tell the gospel truth
    Of a lady singin' By and By
Wide-eyed, alert, and work-worn hands
    Raised high in praise giving honor to God
Thanking the LORD always in word and deed
    And caring for those she loves.

I tell the gospel truth
    Of a strong woman
Kneeling boldly before God
    In search of answers for loved ones
Never forgetting her place
    And always remembering her state.

I tell the gospel truth
    Of a grandmother
Raising her children's young
    To help them to succeed on their own
Teaching me always,
    Even after her rest has come.

A COUSIN I ONCE HAD

I am beckoned unto this spot

A place that I should not

Called by a cousin I once had

He is confused by the sex pot sitting in the kitchen

And now he wants to make a donkey out of me

I do what asked, unaware my actions will be inappropriate

I sat the glass on the table because the slut he sleeps with is

preoccupied

He chases me up the stairs only to be stopped by my Cuz

Who pushed him back

You see, I was supposed to wait on his slut, until she could hold the

glass in her hand

Like the servant he portrays to me

But I don't sleep with her nor do I owe her that respect

I heard her say, "Daddy want to be white."

He smiled, kissed her and grunted

I once knew a cousin

Brown, bold, courageous, and himself

We lost him to Vietnam

A BIRTHDAY STORY

Birthdays come with wishes that sneak up on you,
even when you expect them

Like
snow flakes sitting on your locks
facial cracks present without a smile
age spots lightening up your legs

Looking Back
growing old seemed graceful
family members moving to the beat of their 90 year old drums

Me
I was ten back then listening to their stories
Today I am way over forty
And the aches and pains tell me a new birthday story

AUNTIE'S FIRE

Moist gobs of tissues
exit between her bosom
capturing the waterfall escaping beneath her crooked wig
specks of tissue balls decorate her face
beaded streams burst on her back
gluing skin to clothes
temperature rising

Crumbled tissues
pats her watery eyes
dabs at the geyser pushing from her armpits
confusion
people chattering
fear
thoughts unthinking

Searching
roaming eyes
heavy breathing
light-headedness
shaky hands
wet everywhere
a cooling device — paper plate

Auntie's relief is in sight
she inhales and exhales
waterfall drys up
geyser recede
moisture absorbs into the unknown
"Oh Jesus", "Woo-O-Wee"
The heat flash is over.

For now

PONDER THIS

The thought of never ending love alludes me but the plight of man keeps me awake.

STEPPING INTO THE BATTLE

Warning signs of going against that which is wrong
causes the shake in my hand to write exact words that can change my life, if
they knew I opposed.

Rights are now violated to comfort the needs of those yelling the loudest
forgetting that I too have rights that though I cry no one hears me in order to
listen to those that say they are being violated,
and now, so am I.

Fear rips through me as I write this thing, trying to explain, that you can have
your rights, but don't deny me mine, by leaving me out. I won't conform to
your desires, which never-end of you pushing your desires into my face?
I disagree.

Why should you have the right to disagree with me but I not with you? You
speak of rights cause you want to be accepted by me and my kind who disagree with what you are doing and saying. I never not accepted you, I love
you, but not what you do.

You think that I have to agree with what you do to accept you. No never. Did
you stop loving me cause you didn't like what I do? To each his own, to each
her own, to each their own, to each own.

It's a risk to write this poem, no lie but this I know seems like history favors
the loudest, something must be wrong because my Christian folks seem to
be quiet, and yet, I am not alone, this is a risk I don't take lightly. Lives are
at stake and one is yours.

FOR PEACE AT HOLIDAY MEALS

I'll leave her alone, if she
Don't pick at me
Don't try to be my friend
Don't talk to me
Don't make jokes using my name
Don't look my way
And by all means
Don't sit near me

I'll not bother him, if he
Doesn't call on me to help
Doesn't tell me what to do
Doesn't ask me any questions
Doesn't mock me
Doesn't remind me of when I was a baby
And by all means
Doesn't eat near me at the dinner table

I won't make a scene, if they
Don't bug me to do a stupid dance
Don't make me eat foods I don't like
Don't ask questions about my life
Don't tell me what I should be doing
Don't ask me for money
And by all means
Don't ask me to take Cousin Jessie home

And regardless of all that, I'll still be there,
knowing that Jesus is in control.

MA'S CLOSET

Many colors
Different Sizes
Mixture of Everything
Randomly stuffed into baskets
Clothes fallen over shoes
Dodging wire hangers
Step in clear spots on rug
No expectation of neatness
Purses clump on hooks
Ma's closet
Looking for something to wear

YESTERDAY'S NEWS

Who told you my stories were yesterday's news?
I'm living in a life of present tense right now
Can't see how my past might help,
you're whatever's ahead.
I been where you at, but did some stuff I wish I hadn't
And now I'm alive so you won't make the same mistake
But take a different road, one higher than the one I chose.

Who told you I live in the past and what I know doesn't mean anything today? The past is the past and what has gotten you through to today life is what you make it. Didn't you go through the past to get to today? My past, good or bad, is a foreshadow of your future.
Your mission if you choose to accept it: Change it or not.

The choice is yours. The mistakes yours. Don't follow my mistakes
Follow my success and in that you'll find your own mistakes
Stop making my mistakes. Why? So you can be like I. Or do you think you'll do better? Either way the choice is yours. My past tells me to skip the mistakes and ride off my people's, parents', legacy's' successes because then the mistakes are mine but my people, family, legacy is further than the one behind. What I know is that the choice is yours, pay attention to mine.

Who told you, you were entitled to my stuff but respecting me is too much?
Who told you I care too much but you not enough?
Who told you I am not listening to you when you talk the same crap over and over?
Who told you my words were not fun?

Who told you to stay away from me in order to feel safe?
Who told you my life can't help you advance?
Age is a number but living is a choice.
I'm here

Made it through the lies told,
The lies I lived by
And the lies I busted open wide.
I know the ropes
Ain't nothing new under the sun, even the Bible tells you so

The difference is more peoples being affected
More of what is now that was less of then
And you can't see it now?
Cause you allowed the scroll, swipe, TV watching
while on cellphone, zombie games
To get your attention
Anything shiny, bling bling, or satisfy your desire
But what's real you think kills and is old
Life is worth living, but you can't see
Tied down by social media, TV, and radio
propaganda rushing through your head
Telling you what to think and how you should be

But you aren't woke yet,
Cause you know it all
The young know better, cause it's about here and now and not what been,
You being guided by stupid people on TV, designed by the ambiguous writer
and money supplier behind that screen.
Kids' cartoons, teaching our kids, being injected by frequent culture
malarkey accumulated from a rash of emotions.

But all you see is what you want to see or what you've learned to see

So much goes on behind the scene and even more behind that, recognize that the money suppliers
Are definitely running your mind
Money hunger, living lies, can't see the truth and not looking for it either.

Some of you think that life is supposed to be dramatic. Why not? Isn't it on TV and social media?
That's not life, that's propaganda.
That's giving you what you are conditioned to receive so that ratings can go up and more money suppliers gravitate for the actors pay to increase.

Then you say my stories are old news!
So what will yours be when you get my age
No news or the same news. Oops, I forgot,
Many of you won't make it cause y'all dropping like flies
Not listening to the old people, your heritage and legacy, who done that and been there,
Even some demonstrating before your eyes how not to be like them
There you lay in the coffin cause of suicide, overdose, reckless living, sexual screwed-up-ness,
Arrogance, running after money that was never yours.

And you say my stories are old.
Hope you get to tell yours before it's too late,
Before those coming after you think your present life is too old to listen to
And toss you by the side because your money isn't large enough
Or your money is all they have and they are willing to take it from you.

Now whose stories are too old?

Now come sit with me for a while so we can talk about the good old days.
Yesterday.

Flash Fiction

BY LYVITA BROOKS

FRIENDLY COMPETITION

Competing against the unfinished work of my mother's pen: the concentrated thoughts flowing through the steady glide of her pen, intensified by the line between her eyebrows, I'm fixated by the muse that covers her being as if human to pen to paper are one. The rhythmic taping of pen upon paper ludes me to dreamland, uninhibited by constraints, not moving, thinking, the muse comes to me like rain hitting on a tree leaf, moves me to win, moves me to write. The sound of my mother's pen softens, my muse...zzzzz. Procrastination wins again.

THE JOY OF BECOMING A P&J

As usual, I have to pick up my little cousins because their mother doesn't want to pay for a babysitter. It's not fair being a college student who lives at home. For some reason everyone thinks that they can delegate you to do things, especially my mother.

Here they come. Six-year-old, DayDay, six-and-a-half-year-old, Quincy, and five-year-old Nydie.

"Bidda, Bidda," Nydie runs towards me with that look on her face, mispronouncing my name. The hairs on my neck start to rise as she says, "You got to sit in the middle."

"I'm driving," I say, "Just get in the back and don't do nothing."

She does.

"Vidda," says DayDay, "I want to drive." I just laugh and shove him in the back. He rolls onto the seat laughing.

"I'm not sitting in the middle," Quincy tugs on my blouse. "Can't I sit in the front with you? I'm almost seven."

"No way. You touch things you aren't supposed to," I say, pushing him into the car. "DayDay, move over so Quincy can get in."

DayDay grabs the seat belt and locks himself in. "No!"

"OK, what's the problem?" I say, looking at the three amigos.

"Someone better talk or I'm taking you back to your mother and you know what happened when I did it last time."
"He doesn't want to be peanut butter and jelly," Nydie says.

"What?"

"Come sit here." Nydie pat the seat between the two of them, "It's a secret. Come on Bidda, sit down." So I do.

In unison, I hear three snickering little cousins bellow a song, "Peanut Butter and Jelly, Peanut Butter and Jelly. Vidda is Peanut Butter and Jelly."

I chuckle for a minute. Then made Quincy get in so I could drive.

They sing that stupid song all the way to the movies, even though Quincy rides in the middle.

Although I want to take them back to their mother because they won't stop, I have to admit, the song is catchy.

YOUNG MAMA RUTH

(Why can't I just get my hair done without the stories?)

#1

Girrrl, I tell you a story, short, that you won't believe, but it's true.

(Again?)

It's about Young Mama Ruth, who lived in a boot. A very large boot. Size 12 to be exact. Height came up just above the head. The upper part of the boot contained two floors with two bedrooms and a bathroom each. The heel and toe contained the common quarters, kitchen, living room, dining room, and half bath. The boot was lined with pigskin for easy cleanup and odor resistance. The land around the boot was in a box shape that contained a flower bed in the south, dirt in the west, cars and garage to the east, and the north contained a pathway to the button front door where the shoestrings strung.

Ha ha! But I digress. That's not what this story is about. It's about how Young Mama Ruth went belly-up.

#2

Young Mama Ruth had two children and she didn't know what to do. All her sons were lazy and bad to the bone. Not even their fathers knew what to do. Each left their son at the age of twelve.

Son #2 always knew how to steal Young Mama Ruth's money, even while she slept. He didn't have a job nor tried to get one, but found a hard-working woman who had two children of her own. She thought he loved her, but he

64

loved Young Mama Ruth more. That ain't stop her from moving into a boot cause she needed a home.

Then there is Son #1. He snuck three girls to live in his room. They paid him rent until knucklehead got pregnant and the other two left. Then he claimed he had a job at the Piggy Wiggly. But they don't exist in Pennsylvania. Either way, he ain't never paid Young Mama Ruth nothin'. The knuckleheaded gal married him, so she said. Then the next day a white child and an Asian child came to live with them too. Startled everyone, but they didn't know what to do. So they welcomed the children, Knucklehead grinned and shoed her children to bed. Now every room in the boot was filled to capacity, except the fourth room. It was divided into two. One side slept the boys and the other the girls. Cause each Son had a boy and a girl.

(Now that's just stupid. Where she get these stories? Who'd live in a boot?)

#3

Young Mama Ruth asked Husband #1 what she should do. Too many people living in her boot and soon two more babies gonna pop out, too. Husband #1 gave his opinion and enforced it. The sons gagged him, strung him to the button front door, and tightened it closed. When Young Mama Ruth got home, she released him. He flew without saying a word.

#4

The divorce was final. It took less than a year. Young Mama Ruth now cried to God for relief. Her no-working sons, their women, and gobs of children was too much to bear. A man showed up at her office one day. They fell in love, got married and he left the same day. Young Mama Ruth's sons took him fishing. They drove him to West Virginia, where he's from, left him at the bus station and then they made a run. Till this day Young Mama Ruth don't know why he left, but the divorce papers showed up three months later.

(What city boys go fishin'? Girl, just do my hair and shut up… Oh yeah, it's time to nob like I care.)

#5

She lived with Boyfriend #1. He was cool, besides she needed help. Mortgage was a month behind, the boot flaps needed mending, bills piling up, mouths to feed, and the pigskin in Son #2 room was stinking. Everyone liked Boyfriend #1 including her sons. They left him alone. Then her money ran out and Boyfriend #1 was gone.

(She burned me last time. I hope she's payin' attention and not puttin' that stuff on my scab...'cause I'm about to be gone. Gone up out of here to...chuckle.)

#6

Well, God finally answered her prayer. She met Boyfriend #2, straight from heaven. All liquored-up but time enough for her sons when he wasn't drunk. Young Mama Ruth's sons caught on to that and kept him drunk until they could beat him up. One day, they left him in a bar, called the police, and said he was dead.

Boyfriend #2 believed in God and showed Young Mama Ruth the truth about his Jesus. The sons' tricks never worked, even when they left his drunk behind at the grave site. In Jersey! He kept getting saved with his stink-looking self. So they left him alone and began picking on themselves.

(OK, this is stupid, now. Lord, I need saving.)

#7

Now on this day, which I been trying to get to, something changed. The mortgage bill was due. The light bill too. The heat bill came in. The shoe repair bill too. Every bill, including groceries came due the 4th of this month. Young Mama Ruth was late again on everything. Her disability check wasn't enough to pay them all. She tried payment plans but were behind on them too.

Boyfriend #2 couldn't hold down a job and her sons were lazy to the bone, ignoring her plea. The working girl never offered any money but kept her kids in designer jeans and Knucklehead made no problems but kept her children feed. To top it all off, both gals' babies were due for real this month.

So she gathered up the family, girlfriends too. They talked, fused, talked, cussed, and walked out. Yelled, cussed some more, apologized, fussed, and then gave up. What was Young Mama Ruth to do?

(Put their tails out, like I want out this chair. Oh yeah…smile)

#8

She prayed like Boyfriend #2 said. Then got off her knees and roared, "Get out!"

Son #1, laughed, packed up his crew, and they were gone with Knucklehead crying cause she needed this boot.

Son #2 pointed working woman and her children to the door. Confused, they left, stomping their feet. Son #2 got on his hands and knees, promising to get a job if only Young Mama Ruth let him stay. She did, after all, he was her child.

Boyfriend #2 stayed too. He didn't have anywhere to go and besides he was heaven sent.

(This stupid story got me interested. So what happened next? How the bills get paid?)

#9

Young Mama Ruth cried, "Lord, Please Help!" Boyfriend #2 heard her cries. His love deepened. He called on God. Stopped drinking, found a job, and brought her a ring. Not a real ring, a pretend ring, one you see in your imagination. The lights got cut off, the heat stopped working, and soles began to crack.

Son #2 got an under-the-table paying job and came home the next day with enough cash to pay off everything, even the back taxes. Young Mama Ruth was delighted.

(That don't sound right.)

#10

Girrrl, three weeks later Young Mama Ruth smiled as she came home. Tried as heck from working two jobs and putting out selfish people while trying to stop her boot from walking. That can be exhausting. This day, she came home, opened the door, and the aroma made her hallucinate. She turned around and sat on the stoop. Boyfriend #2 got off the bus and saw her sitting there. He joined her and they laughed, talking about their future possibilities and the real ring he'll get her. This was short-lived because the police showed up, handcuffed Son #2 and took him to jail.

Young Mama Ruth had had enough. Her son was growing a weed garden on the south side of the boot. He was smoking that stuff in her kitchen. That was the odor that forced her out. Well, Girl, he was making some good stuff from the flower bed.

(Whoa ... I was thinkin' about getting' a hit later today.)

#11

I want to say the story ends there, but Young Mama Ruth fell, belly-up. Boyfriend #2 caught her head, and heard her say, "Jesus is my time up?" Then she collapsed. Boyfriend #2 prayed. Then hit her in the chest.

#12

Young Mama Ruth is now resting in bed. She said God told her to stop stressing.

(Is that it? I spent my time listening to another made-up story. Hurry up and finish my hair.)

#13

Now Girrrl, let me end this story before Young Mama Ruth's appointment. *(What ... Oh Snap! She's real.)*

TOUCHÉ

"Get here ASAP!" echoed in my ear through shallow breaths, magnified by the fifteen-minute drive on the icy road home. She ran to my car wearing a torn bathrobe and goofy slippers. I parked. "We're pregnant!" I'm confused. "Riven is having pups!" Seriously, she gives that dog more attention than me.

MY HUSBAND THE MECHANIC

One more time, like a broken record, I hear, "It's ready." Only to discover what we agreed needed fixing wasn't what was done. *Squeak, Squeak ...* I hear. He says, "I fixed what needed to be done now and not later."

I'd walk away shaking my head, "I can't drive my car like that. Lights come on when they want to, windshield wipers leave traces of rubber in my face, tires need rotating, and the hint of smoke rises inside the car, he thinks is less important than putting oil in the car? The car leaks!"

I'm a 75 year old female with all my hair and teeth and can still dance you off the floor. Does he think I'm stupid? If you didn't want to do it, just say so, honey.

LURED

I was a bird nestled in her house. Perched to marry you. Twisted by your manipulative heart. You plucked and bent my wings. Decay began. Deception, lies, exaggerations, and guilt amputated my resolve to fight.

Awakened to the reality of your lack of emotional attachment.

"It's not my fault."

You didn't want me, but my money.

Now I am a bird in flight, with papers to peck you out my life.

"COUGH, COUGH"

A blonde blue-eyed reporter entered Starbucks desperately seeking anyone to answer his question. People ignored him. I waved him over. His eyes widened, walked to my table, presented his credentials and asked, "How do you feel about the changes made in the White House?"

I said, "I'm smothering under the continued lies trying to control me. Denying me from being me. My golden ebony complexion still haunts my lighter-skinned people. The fact that I am female causes a man to compete with me, reject me, or rape the very essence of me. My Christian beliefs are judged, twisted, and offensive all because I don't believe as they do. And oh, my children. The subtle propaganda used to confuse them and strip them from my guidance in an attempt to make me, the parent, look like a fool. Is this democracy? Or double standards?

"Deny me, keep me struggling, guessing, while they strip all of what was America to meet their needs. Is this true for you? Is this the country for the people? Are we all free? Or are the affluent influencers forcing their beliefs on me?

"Double standards.

"You ask how I feel. The White House can't save us. Its goal is to mix us into their melting pot, where our identities are lost—Cough, Cough—depicted as unity.

And yet, I have peace, for my savior is Christ Jesus."

The middle-aged reporter sank in his seat, concern on his face.

Now the lines are drawn.

The conversation begins.

WORKING FOR GOD

I write.

THE STORYTELLER

Do you have that one person in your life that is so memorable until their death became the inspiration of your writing life? I have two. My mother, the poet and my cousin, the larger-than-life storyteller.

The Storyteller is dead, five months before her 50th birthday. All I remember are the stories she told which held our attention like a bear with honey. My two cousins and I were convinced that Ivy Jean could make a donkey sit still and listen to her stories. My mother, on the other hand, often said, "Ivy Jean tells make-believe stories and y'all believe anything coming out of her mouth."

Growing up, every summer and holidays, my cousins and I would gather around Ivy Jean upstairs in her bedroom listening intently to her stories as she sat on her bed painting the teeny tiny nails on her fluffy toes. We couldn't wait to hear another one of her adventures. She knew everything, especially about boys. We were high schoolers, what else were we to talk about? Books?

I remember quite vividly one summer when we were going to our first dance in Philadelphia, which was considered the hip place to be. As usual, Ivy Jean was the center of our attention, and we knew a story was brewing. She flicked her fake blonde hair behind her shoulder and began...

"The boys in Philly are so much better than the ones in Yeadon," Ivy Jean said. "All the parties have more boys than girls. I always have a problem trying to figure out who to give my phone number to."

My cousin and I began rapidly firing questions at Ivy Jean. We asked, "Are the boys cuter? Will they have food? Do we have to slow dance because boys can get smelly? What will they have to drink? Do I look alright?"

Ivy Jean was never amazed or flustered by our questions. She answered them in story-like form, "The boys are more fun in Philly. We should have food and drinks but don't eat or drink till I tell you it's OK. Sometimes they put hash in the food and spike the punch with Whiskey. I have ..."

My mother interrupted, "Ivy Jean, have you ever attended a party in Philly?"

"No," Ivy Jean said without skipping a beat or understanding the significance of my mother's question. "I have heard you can have a lot of fun. I'll tell you which boys to dance with and what to do so you won't be scared."

We should have realized then that she was lying but her stories didn't leave room for intelligent thinking. Like when she told us this boy liked her but he crossed the street in front of her house without looking our way. "We talk in school," she said.

Every time I think about her, I laugh. She filled my cousins and me with such wonderment and delight. When my mother told me that Ivy Jean passed, of course I didn't believe her. Not my teller-of-great-stories cousin. Reality can be a hard pill to swallow when your throat tightens. This was one of those moments. How, why, what happened, questions flowed through my brain cycling around until they were silenced by my mother saying, "I just talked to her minutes before she died going up the stairs."

Her defibrillator didn't have enough power to restart her heart. Her heart had told her last story. She left us with great stories, whether fiction or non-fiction and the belief that life is what you dream it. I am a writer today because I grew up believing in a world of imagination created by Ivy Jean, the Storyteller and my mother, the reflective poet.

True this story isn't complete, but I had to share how God blessed me with people who not only helped me grow as a writer, but also keep it real. Now it's your turn. Who has inspired or helped you grow into using the gift or talent God's given you? Take time to thank them and whatever you do, if you promise them something, then do it!

At The End Begins Another's Future

TRANSITIONING

What does it mean?
"Your mother's transitioning?"

Was I supposed to flee to her side?
She passed before I arrived.

Am I guilty of something?
I did everything possible.

God said,
"I'm taking my daughter home."

Jesus was by her side
She didn't go to heaven alone.

Isn't that transitioning?
Why do I feel guilty?

I told her everything on my heart
I told her how much I love her and I'd be OK.

Why do I feel guilty?
Why do I feel sad?
Why do I feel alone?

Her journey ended and her shoes are hard to fill
They were already done but her memories linger on.

Now it's my time to transition
To pivot
I don't continue alone.

MA HAS LEFT

Clothes everywhere
Proof Ma's been in this room

Nothing washed
Dishes in sink
Restaurant containers bunched in frig
Proof Ma's been in this room

Food particles floating in half-full glass,
Sitting next to an empty chair
Food droppings everywhere
Rat watching TV near her chair
Proof Ma's been in this room

Shoes pushed under the bed
Curtains opened wide
Adjustable bed
Tubes in her insides
Proof Ma's living in this room

Different body temperatures
Linen clean
Bed flattened
Machines off
No tubes insight
Proof Ma's left this room

I HAVE MOMENTS

I sit here … I cry

Some days I want Ma back

And other days I just want her

She's left me here

I'm settled with that now

Jesus's got her

It's just that the memories keep…flowing back.

Going to call her

Remembering I can't

Wrapping myself in blankets

Her blankets that kept her warm

Now they keep me warm

Now they keep me safe

I ask Jesus to wake her up to tell her

"Happy Mother's Day"

His smile tells me that she already know it

I'm settled about her leaving me

Jesus's got her

I'll catch up with them

In another moment in time.

WHEN WILL IT BE MY TURN?

(BY LYVITA BROOKS' NEXT MAIN CHARACTER, DESIREE)

She's always promising. First her Ma and now me.

I'm broken, between, the "what if's" and "what was". (Change can do that to you, I thought.) She's been through shingles, passing of her mother, pneumonia, job change, and now, she can't seem to get me together. Always changing me, I'm likeable today, fighting someone tomorrow, or adding what I can do after striking out what I did do. Even though I guide her through my story on many sleepless nights, she still awakes mixed up.

"Take time with me," I heard Him tell her that. (That's her God, I thought.) She tried but got so caught up in the quiet until she fell asleep and dreamed about somebody else. "Augh," she heard me yell. It startled her. She stopped and listen. "Maybe, if I get to Him. He'll help me out, too." No need, He's on it. I guess He doesn't want me to die in the fossil pile of her mind, all bones and no meat. It's time for me to be released. There are many others waiting to get through.

She's writing about me again! He loves me too. (Her Jesus has many more stories for her to tell, even after me, I thought.) Yesterday we laughed on the back porch and last night, she scribbled my world in her journal. It's been over seven years that she's bathe me in prayers and wrote my story. If it were not for Him, my writer would not have created me, as promised.

Finally, I'm Desiree.

Lyvita's first short story to publish, next.

As promised.

"IT'S BEEN A GREAT JOURNEY"

WORDS FROM VERDELL REESE, WRITTEN BY LYVITA BROOKS

"I didn't expect to leave you at this time, but my Savior had another plan. God knows what He is doing! You will be alright because I have prayed for you in some way or another. In all you do, make sure you get to know Jesus Christ and He will show you how to best live your life.

"Don't just know His name and a few verses here or there, but develop a relationship where you talk to Him even when you don't need nothing from Him.

"Take courage and forgive others, support others, love your family even when they don't love you, and love others. When you ask Jesus, He'll give you the strength to. Just read His word, do what it says, and listen. Practice this. As you grow, so will your understanding of who He is.

"I have passed you the torch which contains reflections from my life, poems, and stories my daughter just had to tell. Now you. Yes, *you*. Run on. Run on without me, without those whom you have loved and cherished, those of us who have gone on.

"Let Jesus Christ be your choice. And giving up is *not* an option!"

Resources

Other Bible Studies by Lyvita Brooks
www.themeprojectacademy.com

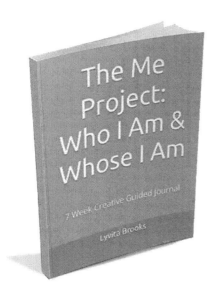

7-Week creative guided Bible study journal about developing a lasting and consistent relationship with God. Great for new Christians and seasoned believers needing to rekindle their relationship with God and others, 131 pages, 8 x 12 size.

The Me Project Took Kit provides resources designed to help you begin developing a relationship with God and establishing a schedule for growth.

Afterword

Bible Studies, Classes & Coaching: The Me Project Academy contains practical tips for growing in Christ, Bible studies, inspiration, challenges, and more. The Academy is focused on helping you apply what you are learning in Christ so you can live a more spiritually disciplined life in Christ. www.themeprojectacademy.com

Website: www.lyvitabrooks.com contains information about Hanging Out With Jesus Podcast, blog, book reviews, and The Me Project Academy. It's the place where you can find everything, including other books, notebooks, and journals written by this author.

Podcast: *Hanging Out With Jesus Podcast* is about helping believers stand for Christ living in a collapsing culture. www.hangingoutwithjesuspodcast.com

Newsletter: *The Me Project Academy Newsletter* contains practical tips for growing in and standing for Christ, practicing spiritual disciplines, inspiration, challenges, prayer and more. Focused on helping you live a purpose-filled life in Christ. www.lyvitabrooks.com/subscribe

Instagram: @hangingoutwithjesuspodcast contains inspiration, highlights from podcast episodes and more.

Pinterest: @themeprojectacademy focuses on practical tips for growing in Christ using spiritual disciplines.

If you enjoyed this book, please consider posting a review wherever you purchased the book or perhaps on Goodreads.com, too. Even if it's only a few sentences, it would be greatly appreciated. Thank You!

READY TO FIND YOUR NEXT GREAT
BOOK OR BIBLE STUDY?

LET US HELP.

Visit
https://lyvitabrooks.com/store

About The Author

Lyvita Brooks loves hanging out with Jesus, which is the name of her podcast, *Hanging Out With Jesus Podcast*. She's also an author, poet, speaker, blogger and founder of The Me Project Academy. As a retired school system educator and administrator she still enjoys teaching Bible study. At the age of twenty-one she met Christ Jesus and learned who she was, whose she was and why she was. This forged an everlasting relationship between God Almighty and His child, Lyvita, through His Son, Lord Jesus The Christ, guided by the Holy Spirit. Growing up in Beulah Baptist Church, she realized the importance of <u>developing spiritual disciplines</u> in her life to help keep her focused and sane in a chaotic world.

Her mission is to help believers live a clutter-free life, through implementing spiritual disciplines, in order to Go & Do what God's designed them to do. This is her reason for putting together tools and resources to help you do the same. Lyvita has a passion for building up the body of Christ, the saints, to be all God's called them to be. And to God be the glory!

Made in the USA
Middletown, DE
14 January 2024

47566261R00059